CONTENTS

D1648480

OVERVIEW

These songs are ideal for use in EVERY type of Primary School assembly. Whilst many have a 'mainly Christian' emphasis, all the songs are enjoyable, varied and relevant! We are sure they will be useful and appreciated in any context. Most of all, they are great fun to sing!

WAKE UP!
A lively start to the day/week/project! Written for younger children, with lots of scope for actions. (The lyrics make these self-explanatory). *Scope for music composition activities -eg- sounds we wake up to, and for discussion about different times of the day (likes/dislikes, sequence of events).*

TOGETHER
An easy song for KS1 which captures the value and fun of doing things 'as one'! *For discussion: what are the difficulties/benefits of doing things together? Personal examples? Suggested story links?*

WE LIKE JOYFUL MUSIC!
A carnival style song, written for KS1&2 celebrating the joy of music. Older children will enjoy the option of two-part singing towards the end. *An interesting song for the children to interpret visually in paints/colours etc.. For discussion: "..reasons to be happy!"*

LIVING AND LEARNING
This song has a strong African flavour, written in the rhythm of a working song. It addresses the theme of natural life cycles. Dynamics can be used to great effect in the singing of this song. (Try experimenting!) *Plenty of imagery to discuss and develop ideas of constancy and change.*

EVERYWHERE AROUND ME
A lively song with a strong theme. Asks questions about creation and expresses wonder at creative design and order. *Invites artistic work as a follow-up eg. collage/design - 'pattern and colour', 'wonders of nature' etc. Obvious RE links.*

SONG OF BLESSING
A simple reflective song which can be sung as a prayer for the teachers, helpers and for the children. Suitable for solos/group singing.

COUNT YOUR BLESSINGS
A fun song with a positive reminder to be grateful for what we have. Written in Caribbean style, with a definite lilt! Whilst the youngest of children can enjoy this song sung straight through, it is intended to be sung as a round.

SOMETIMES I WONDER
The sad song of the project, addressing the issue of pain and suffering. A thoughtful song with a message of hope. Helpful perhaps for times of corporate sadness/bereavement/loss etc.

cont'd...

THE SCHOOL RULE SONG

A fun song with a serious edge. The subject of "do's and don'ts" is presented in a 'call and response' song in Israeli/Greek style! *Lots of scope for discussion about rules and regulations. Children could write their own 'Classroom Rules'. An ideal song to present dramatically.*

LOVE THE LORD YOUR GOD

From the teachings of Jesus, this 'Scripture-Memory-Song' brings the Biblical message bang up to date in a rock shuffle rendition. Can be sung in parts where appropriate. *Before using the song: What would the children consider to be the single most important rule/law to live by? This song lends itself to a choreographed dance routine.*

HE'LL BE THERE

A very catchy, lively tune with a 'reggae' feel, intended for use by KS1&2. The chorus provides scope for harmony and echoes. A happy and easy-going song with a simple theme. *Valuable links with geography, (places/travel/transport) and RE themes (being lost, solitude etc).*

WOULDN'T IT BE FUNNY...?

The 'peculiar' song! Thought-provoking ideas in a quirky style. (Spot the snippets of nursery rhymes). *A real gift for creative discussion and artwork. (How would it be if the sky were green/fish could fly/if we had two mouths? etc. What makes humans different from animals?) An interesting way in to questions of design and order. Also a great song to paint!*

GIVE IT ALL YOU'VE GOT!

The 'happening' dance track for the 90's, which can be used as a personalised school theme song. (The chorus requires you to fit the name of your school into the lyrics). This positive message is presented in a spoken rhythmic 'rap' style. Ideal for KS2, but the younger ones will love to join in the chorus and the repeated 'chant and clap' ('Give it 1, Give it 2, Give it 1, 2, 3!'). You'll need the backing track for this one. Just be sure to boost the bass and treble controls, and give it all the volume you've got!

WELL DONE!

The 'congratulations' track. Written to celebrate any kind of success, effort or achievement. Two versions of the lyrics to this song are supplied - one to acknowledge competitive success, and the other to congratulate individual or team achievement/effort. A fast, fun song!

TODAY

A very simple but reflective song, in a mellow mood. A short five-liner that expresses a desire to make the day count through care, kindness and love. A good song to quieten things down, and an appropriate one with which to finish.

WAKE UP!

CHORUS   *Wake up! Wake up!*
Give yourself a shake up,
Get your body moving.
Reach up, jump up,
Give your friend the 'thumbs up'!
It's another new day!   (Repeat)

1   Get your feet
Dancing to the beat,
Get your body moving.
Raise a shout! (HEY!)
Let your feelings out,
It's another new day!

CHORUS

Repeat verse 1

HALF CHORUS INSTRUMENTAL

Verse 1 through twice (repeat last line)

WAKE UP!

Words & Music by
MARK and HELEN JOHNSON

4

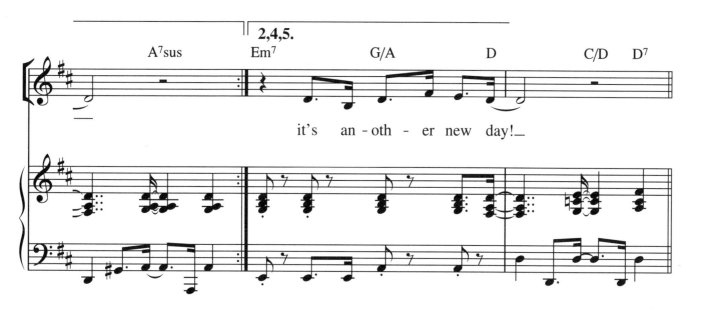

2,4,5.

it's an-oth-er new day!_

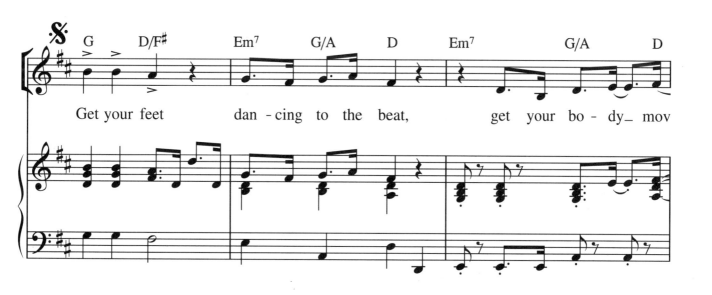

Get your feet dan-cing to the beat, get your bo-dy_ mov

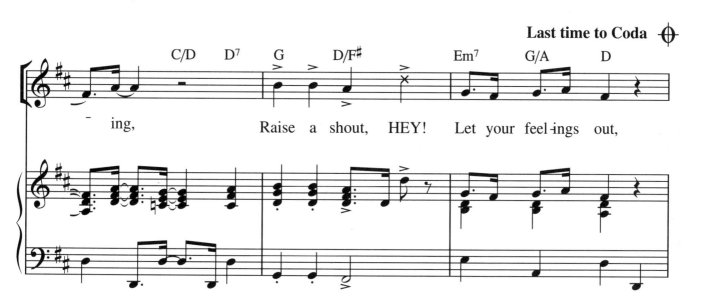

Last time to Coda

-ing, Raise a shout, HEY! Let your feel-ings out,

5

TOGETHER

1   We are <u>here</u> together, together, together,
     We are here together, everyone.

2   What we <u>do</u> together, together, together,
     What we do together, we do as one.

     CHORUS   *Every day, we work and play,*
                  Learning ways to get along.
                  Finding out, what life's about,
                  Everybody moving on.

3   When we <u>play</u> together, together, together,
     When we play together, it's so much fun!

4   When we <u>work</u> together, together, together,
     When we work together, the job get's done!

     CHORUS

5   When we <u>sing</u> together, together, together,
     When we sing together, the beat goes on!

6   When we <u>move</u> together, together, together,
     When we move together, it keeps us strong!

     CHORUS

7   Put your <u>hands</u> together, together, together,
     Put your hands together, everyone!

8   Repeat verse 1

TOGETHER

Words & Music by
MARK and HELEN JOHNSON

In a groove ♩=104

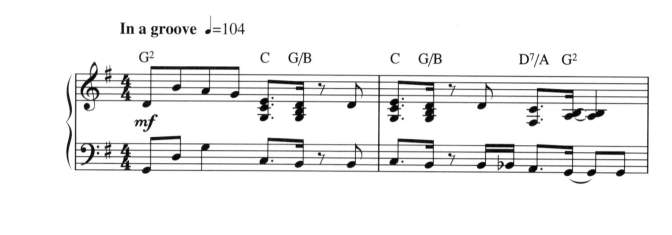

1.We are here to -geth - er, to-
3.When we play to -geth er, to-
5.When we sing to -geth - er, to-
7.Put your hands to -geth - er, to-

geth- er, to -geth- er, we are here to -geth-er, ev' ry - one._
geth- er, to -geth- er, when we play to -geth-er, it's so much_ fun!
geth- er, to -geth- er, when we sing to -geth-er, the beat goes_ on!_
geth- er, to -geth- er, put your hands to -geth-er, ev' ry - one._

8

2.What we do to -geth - er, to - geth - er, to - geth - er,
4.When we work to -geth - er, to - geth - er, to - geth - er,
6.When we move to geth - er, to geth - er, to - geth - er,
8.Put your hands to -geth - er, to - geth - er, to - geth - er,

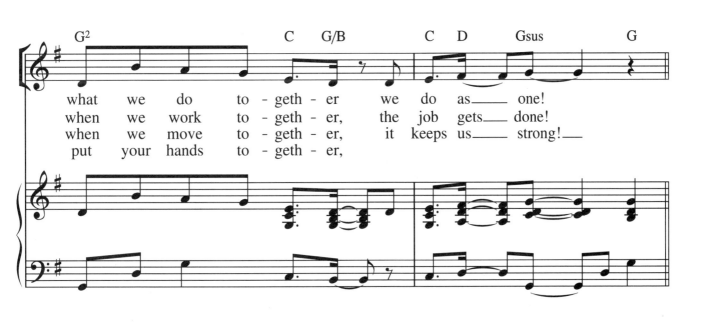

what we do to - geth - er we do as___ one!
when we work to - geth - er, the job gets__ done!
when we move to - geth - er, it keeps us___ strong!__
put your hands to - geth - er,

Chorus

Ev'- ry_ day we work and play, learn - ing ways to get a-long;

Find ing out, what life's a - bout,

ev' - ry - bo - dy mov-ing on.

1,2 **3** *D.S. al Coda*

CODA

put your hands to -geth - er, ev'- ry - one!

10

WE LIKE JOYFUL MUSIC!

1   We like joyful music,
     Full of fun and syncopation,
     And every time we use it,
     Life becomes a song.

2   We like joyful music,
     Full of life and celebration,
     We love the way it moves us,
     When we sing along!

     CHORUS   *Sing with happiness and celebrate!*
                     Let the music fill your heart again! (Repeat)

3   We have all been given,
     Songs to keep our hearts rejoicing,
     The melody and rhythm
     Make the day a 'hit'.

4   We have all been given
     Lots of reasons to be happy.
     Life is made for living,
     Make the most of it!

CHORUS

Repeat verses 1 and 2 over chorus.

CHORUS

WE LIKE JOYFUL MUSIC!

Words & Music by
MARK and HELEN JOHNSON

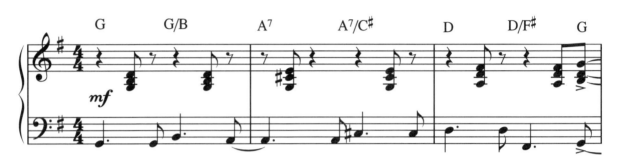

1.We like joy - ful mus - ic,
3.We have all been giv - en,
5.*Repeat verse 1 with Chorus over*

full of fun and syn - co - pa - tion, and ev' - ry time we use
songs to keep our hearts re - joic - ing, the mel - o - dy and rhy-

it,   life be-comes   a   song!
thm,   make the day___ a   'hit'!

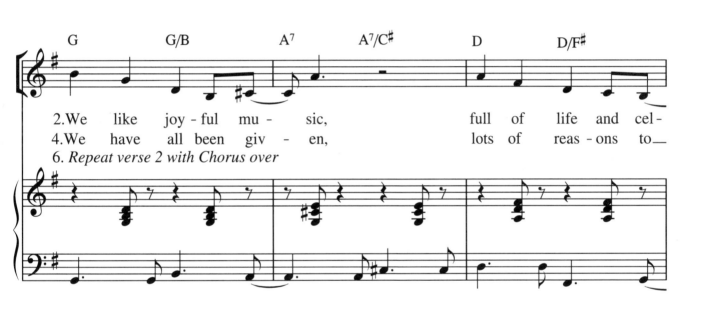

2.We   like   joy - ful mu -   sic,   full   of   life   and cel -
4.We   have   all been giv - en,   lots of reas - ons to___
6. *Repeat verse 2 with Chorus over*

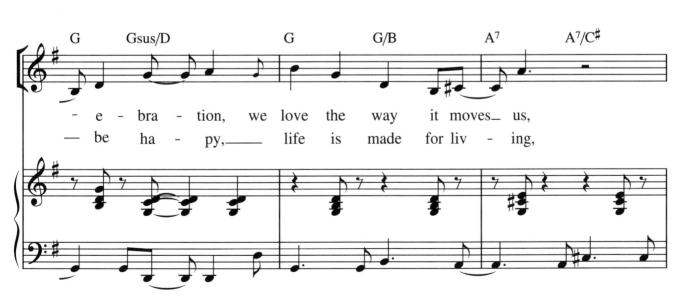

- e - bra - tion, we love the way   it moves___ us,
— be ha - py,___ life is made for liv - ing,

13

14

LIVING AND LEARNING

1   Sun up in the morning,
      Time to get a-moving,
      There's a day for living and there's work to be done.
      Minutes turn to hours,
      Seeds becoming flowers,
      Everything around us is a-moving along.

         CHORUS   *THE EARTH IT KEEP(S) TURNING,*
                   Everything around us is a-moving along.
                   WE'RE LIVING AND LEARNING,
                   Living and a-learning as the day goes on.

2   Getting on together,
      Helping one another,
      Living in the rhythm as we journey on.
      Summer into winter,
      Streams becoming rivers,
      Everything around us is a-moving along.

         CHORUS

3   Changing and a-growing,
      Coming and a-going,
      Everyone together living under the sun.
      Morning turns to evening,
      Sowing turns to reaping,
      Everything around us is a-moving along.

         CHORUS TWICE

4   Repeat verse 1

LIVING AND LEARNING

Words & Music by
MARK and HELEN JOHNSON

In an 'African' style ♩=160

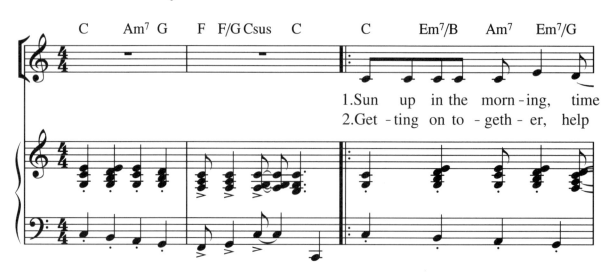

1.Sun up in the morn-ing, time
2.Get-ting on to-geth-er, help

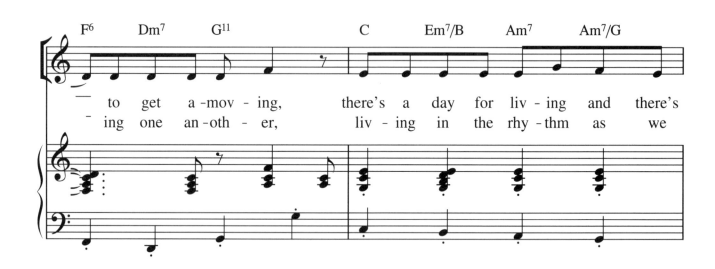

— to get a-mov-ing, there's a day for liv-ing and there's
-ing one an-oth-er, liv-ing in the rhy-thm as we

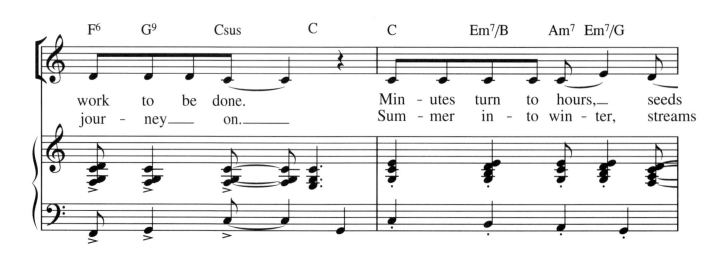

work to be done.
jour-ney on.

Min-utes turn to hours,— seeds
Sum-mer in-to win-ter, streams

17

19

EVERYWHERE AROUND ME

1. Tell me who made all of creation?
   Who designed the wonders of nature?
   Whose idea was pattern and colour,
   Wonderful to see?

   CHORUS   *Everywhere around me,*
   I can see the hand of God,
   The evidence surrounds me,
   In the greatness of His world.
   (Repeat)

2. Tell me who made music and laughter?
   Who designed our bodies to start with?
   Whose idea was thinking and feeling?
   Who gave life to me?

   CHORUS

3. Don't stop looking, don't stop believing,
   God is to be found when you seek Him.
   All creation tells of His glory,
   For eternity.

   LAST CHORUS
   Everywhere around me,
   I can see the hand of God,
   The evidence surrounds me,
   In the greatness of His world.
   (Repeat)
   Everywhere around me!

EVERYWHERE AROUND ME

Words & Music by
MARK and HELEN JOHNSON

With pace ♩=144

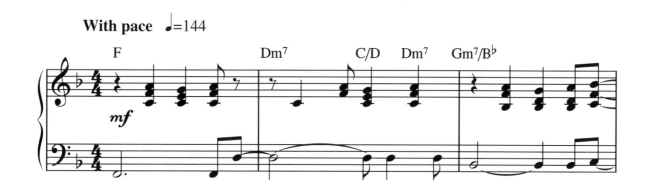

1.Tell me who made all___ of cre - a - tion,
2.Tell me who made mus - ic and laugh - ter,
3.Don't stop look-ing, don't___ stop be - liev - ing,

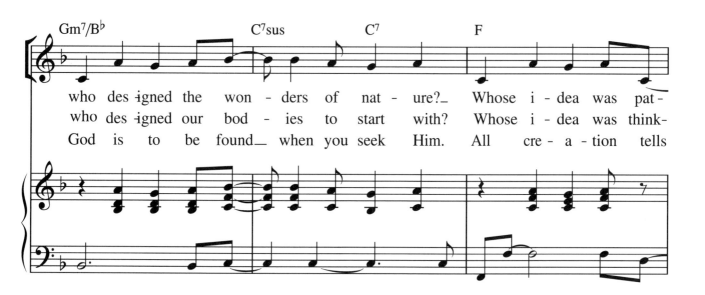

who des - igned the won - ders of nat - ure?_ Whose i - dea was pat -
who des - igned our bod - ies to start with? Whose i - dea was think-
God is to be found_ when you seek Him. All cre - a - tion tells

21

1,2.   *To Chorus*

tern and col - our,   won-der - ful__ to   see?__   Ev' - ry- where a -
ing and feel - ing,   who gave life__ to   me?__   Ev' - ry- where a -
__ of His glo - ry,   for et - er - ni - ty.__

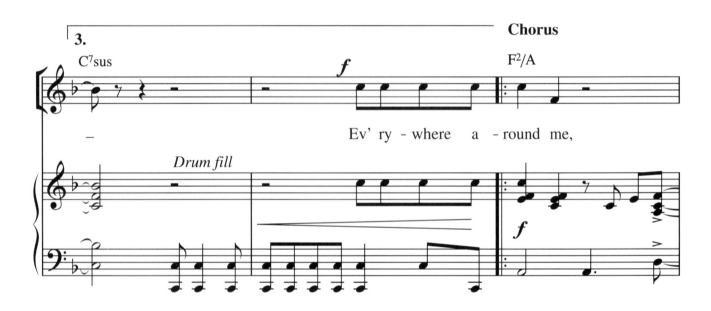

3.   **Chorus**

Ev' ry - where   a - round me,

Drum fill

I can see the hand of   God,__   the ev - i - dence sur-

rounds me, in the great - ness of___ His world.

1,3,5. **2,4.** *To Verse*

Ev' - ry - where a -

D.S.

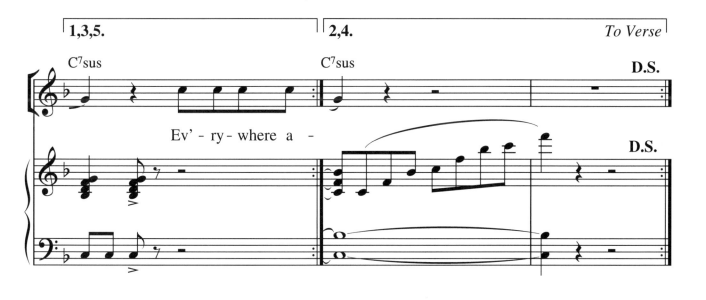

6.

ff Csus F

Ev' - ry - where a -round me!

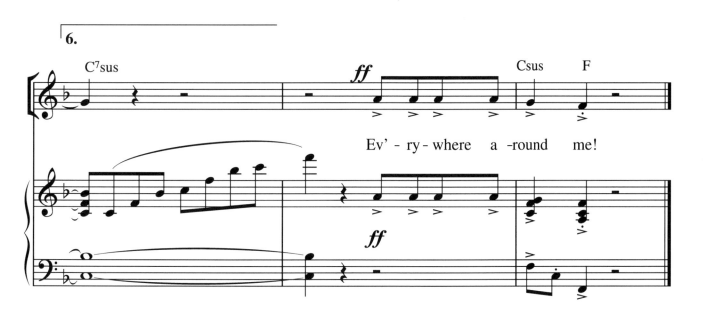

SONG OF BLESSING

1   May God bless our teachers,
     And all our helpers.
     May God show His goodness in all that they do.
     We ask for the children
     That God's hand be on them,
     And may we find His love in this school.

2   (As above)
     ..And may we find His peace in this school.

3   (As above)
     ..And may we find His joy in this school.

SONG OF BLESSING

Words & Music by
MARK and HELEN JOHNSON

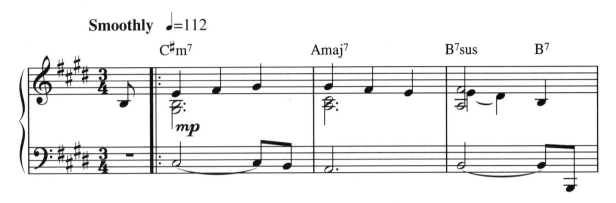

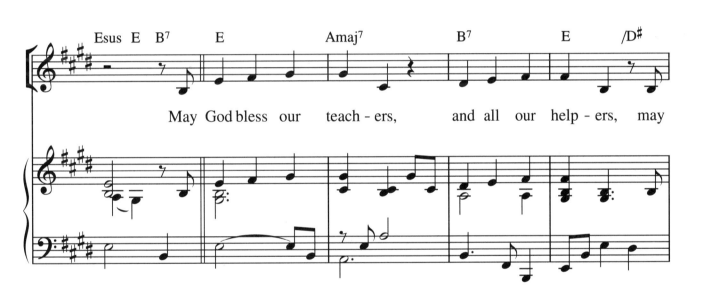

May God bless our teach-ers, and all our help-ers, may

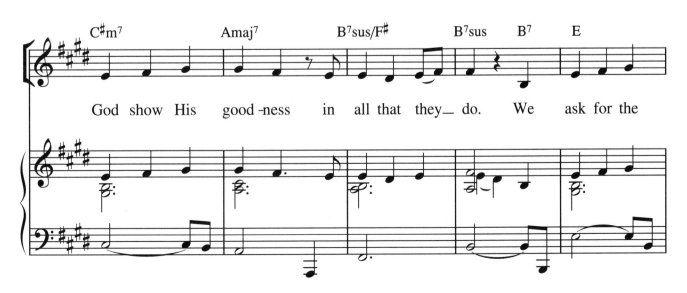

God show His good-ness in all that they_ do. We ask for the

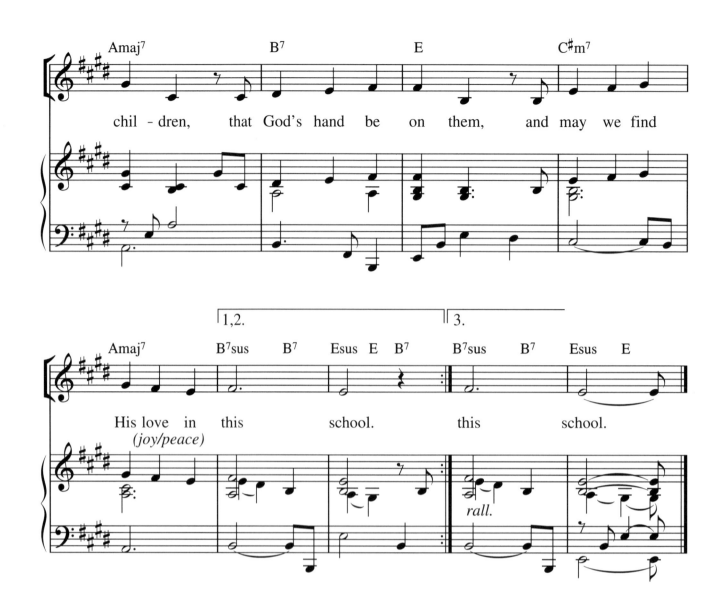

COUNT YOUR BLESSINGS

To be sung as a round

1   If you're feeling sad and weary and you're down in the dumps,
Down in the dumps, down in the dumps,
If you're feeling sad and weary and you're down in the dumps,
There's something you can do:

2   Don't be grumpy,
Don't go on and on.
Don't be grumpy,
Don't you spoil the fun!

3   Count your blessings,
Name them one by one.
Count your blessings,
See what God has done.

COUNT YOUR BLESSINGS

(A Round)

Words & Music by
MARK and HELEN JOHNSON

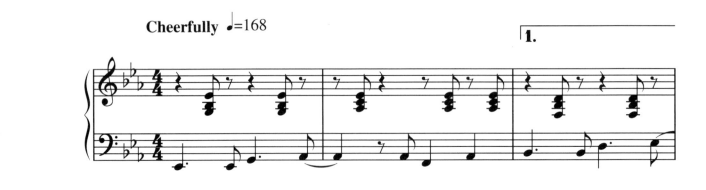

*Sing the whole song through in unison first,
then divide into groups to sing it as a round.*

If you're feel-ing sad and wea-ry and you're *(Part 1)*

Don't be grump- *(Part 2)*

Count your bless- *(Part 3)*

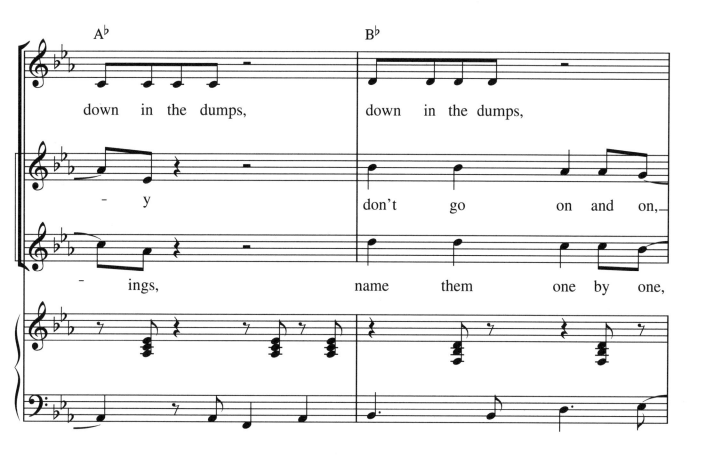

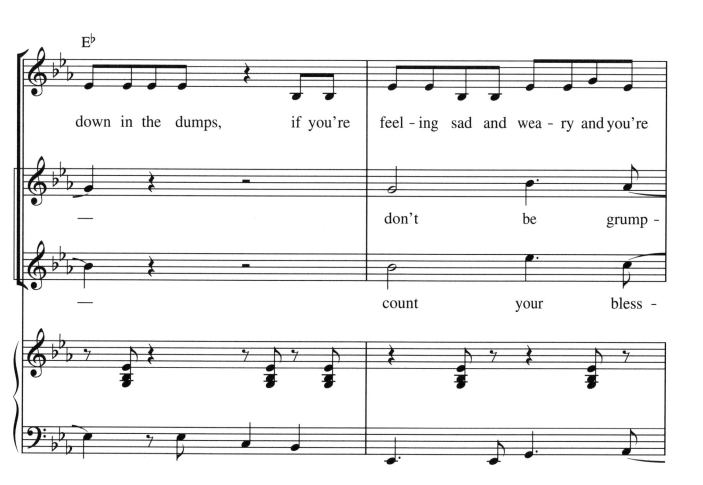

29

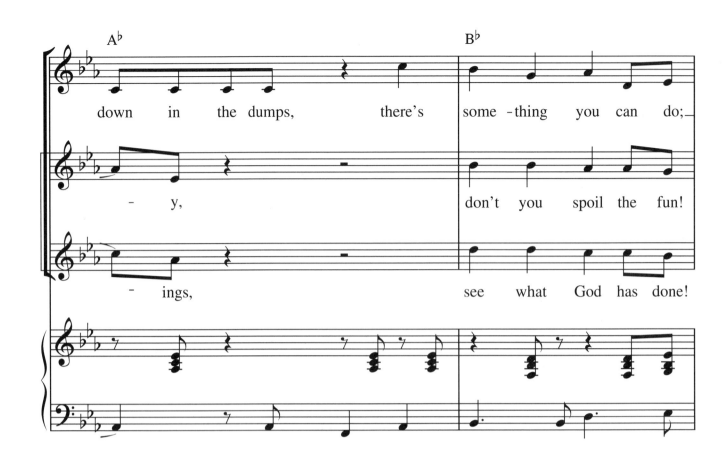

30

SOMETIMES I WONDER

(The Suffering Song)

1   Sometimes I wonder
Why people suffer,
Why all the pain and sorrow?
So much injustice
Weeping and sadness,
Here in our world today.

    CHORUS   *Pain won't be here forever,*
Sadness will turn to laughter,
Mourning will turn to dancing
And our tears will be wiped away.

2   Looking around me
I see such anger,
Why must we hurt each other?
So many people
Living in sadness,
Here in our world today.

    CHORUS

3   INSTRUMENTAL

    CHORUS

4   Where there is heartache,
Where there is grieving,
I want to feel compassion.
May I give comfort
Where there is hurting,
May I bring love again.

SOMETIMES I WONDER

Words & Music by
MARK and HELEN JOHNSON

1.Some - times I won - der, why peo - ple suf - fer,
2.Look - ing a - round me, I see such an - ger,
3.INSTRUMENTAL
4.Where there is heart - ache, where there is griev - ing,

why all the pain and sor - row? So much in - just - ice,
why must we hurt each oth - er? So ma - ny peo - ple,
I want to feel com - pas - sion, may I give com - fort,

Last time to Coda ⊕

weep - ing and sad - ness, here in our world to - day.
liv - ing in sad - ness, here in our world to - day.
where there is hurt - ing,

Chorus

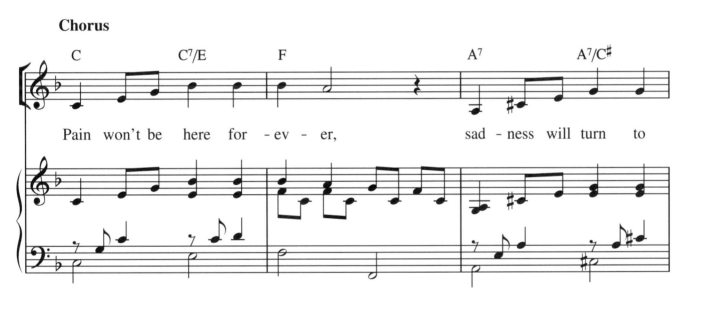

Pain won't be here for - ev - er, sad - ness will turn to

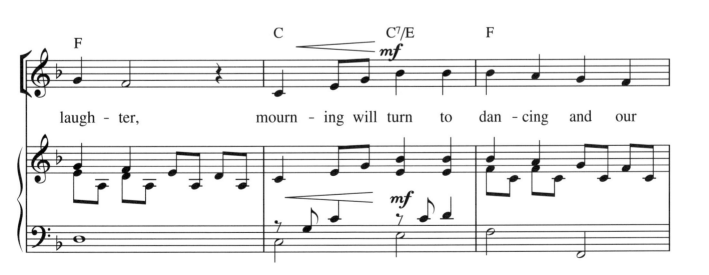

laugh - ter, mourn - ing will turn to dan - cing and our

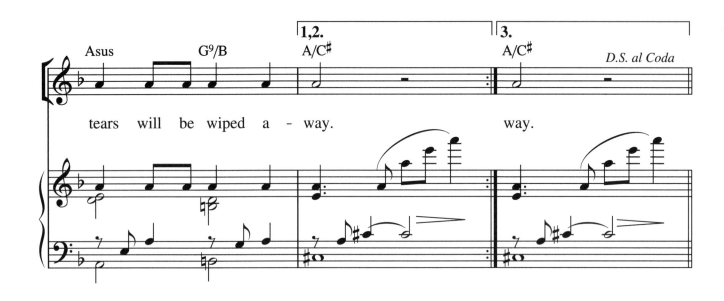

tears   will   be   wiped   a - way.   way.

CODA

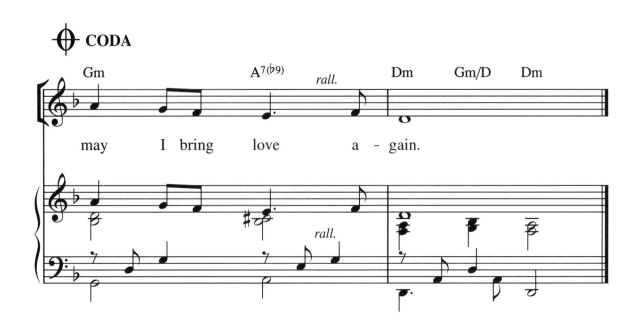

may   I   bring   love   a - gain.

THE SCHOOL RULE SONG

INTRODUCTION
This is an important matter,
How we should behave at school,
We will get along when we obey the rules....

1   Put your hand up, don't call out,
Sit up straight and please don't shout,
We're learning, we're learning.
Please stop talking all the time,
Don't go pushing in the line,
We're learning, we're learning.

CHORUS   *This is an important matter,*
How we should behave at school.
We will get along much better,
When we can obey the rules.

2   Don't run down the corridors,
Don't leave rubbish on the floor,
We're learning, we're learning.
Don't go kicking, never punch,
Watch your manners, eat your lunch,
We're learning, we're learning.

CHORUS

3   Don't tell tales and don't tell lies,
Don't be cheeky or unkind,
We're learning, we're learning.
Treat each other with respect,
Always try to do your best,
We're learning, we're learning.

CHORUS THROUGH TWICE

LAST CHORUS
La, la, la, la, la, la, la, la, etc...

THE SCHOOL RULE SONG

Words & Music by
MARK and HELEN JOHNSON

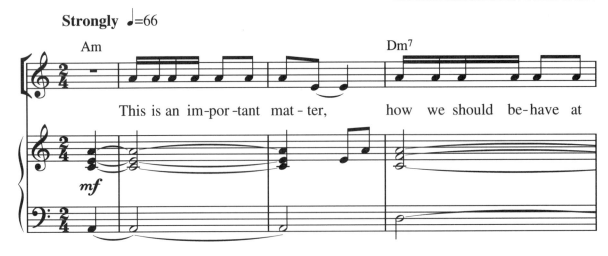

This is an im-por-tant mat-ter, how we should be-have at

school, we will get a-long when we o-bey the rules!

accelerando

Crisply ♩=80 -120

Getting faster each verse

1.Put your hand up, don't call out, sit up straight and
2.Don't run down the cor-ri-dors, don't leave rub-bish
3.Don't tell tales and don't tell lies, don't be cheek-y

36

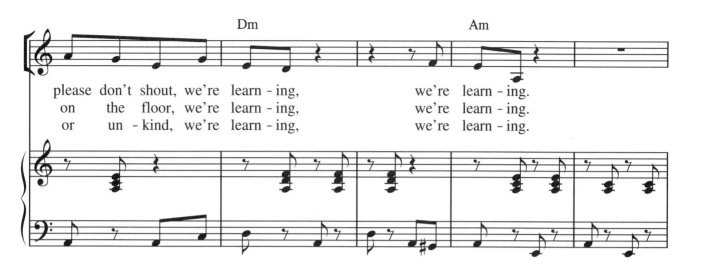

please don't shout, we're learn - ing,   we're learn - ing.
on   the   floor, we're learn - ing,   we're learn - ing.
or   un - kind, we're learn - ing,   we're learn - ing.

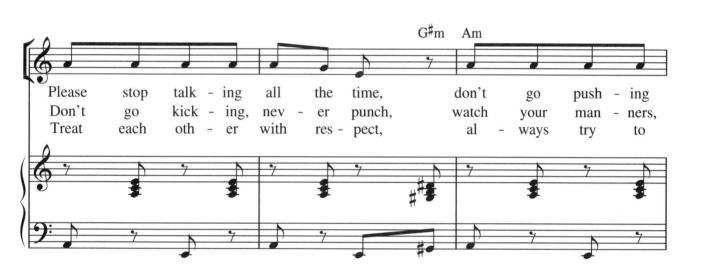

Please   stop   talk - ing   all   the   time,   don't   go   push - ing
Don't   go   kick - ing, nev - er   punch,   watch   your   man - ners,
Treat   each   oth – er   with   res - pect,   al – ways   try   to

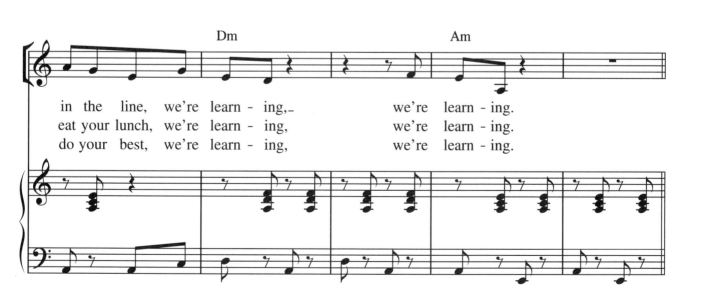

in   the   line,   we're learn - ing,_   we're learn - ing.
eat your lunch, we're learn - ing,   we're learn - ing.
do your best, we're learn - ing,   we're learn - ing.

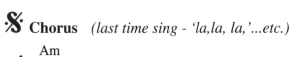

Chorus *(last time sing - 'la,la, la,'...etc.)*

This is an im-por-tant mat - ter, how we should be-have at school,

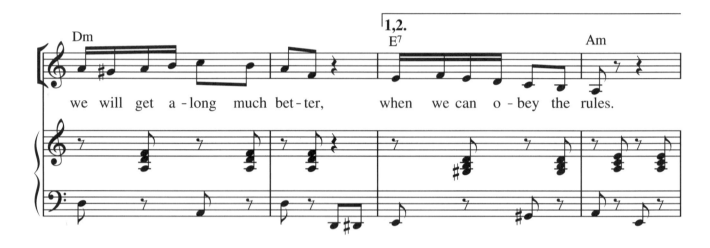

we will get a - long much bet-ter, when we can o - bey the rules.

when we can o-bey the

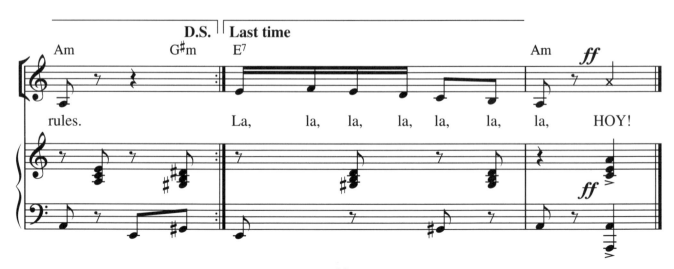

rules. La, la, la, la, la, la, la, HOY!

LOVE THE LORD YOUR GOD

1   Matt- hew, Twenty Two,
    Verses thirty-four to forty. (Repeat)

2   One day a Pharisee
    Came to Jesus Christ and he said
    "Tell me what's the greatest commandment?" (Repeat)

This is what He said:

3   Love the Lord your God
    With all your heart,
    With all your soul,
    With all your mind,
    With all your strength. (Repeat)

4   Love your neighbour as yourself,
    And do to others as you'd have them do to you. (Repeat)

    Parts 3 and 4 together

    Parts 2, 3 and 4 together

LOVE THE LORD YOUR GOD

Words & Music by
MARK and HELEN JOHNSON

Use of backing tracks might be preferable for this song, so as to give full attention to the part-singing

With a swing ♩=140

Mat -thew twen - ty two,
(Spoken in rhythm)

ver-ses thir- ty four to for - ty.— One day a Phar - i - see

came to Jes-us Christ and he said,'tell me what's the great-est com-mand

- ment?'— This is what he said:

E /D /C# /B

A /F# /E /F#

1.Love the Lord your God with all your
(1st, 3rd and 4th time))

2.Love your neigh - bour,
(2nd, 3rd and 4th time)

3.One day a Phar - i - see
(4th time only)

4. Mat - thew
(4th time only - optional)

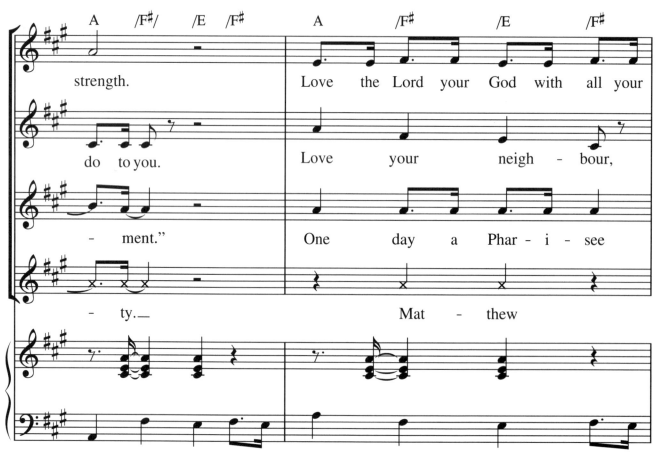

HE'LL BE THERE

(Based on Psalm 139)

1   If I go to the furthest place that I could go,
He'll be there, He'll be there,
To the east or the west, to the sun or snow,
He will always be there!

        CHORUS   *OH YEAH!*
OH YEAH!
He will never leave me.
I KNOW!
HE CARES!
He's the only one I know who's always there!

2   In the dark of the night or in the light of day,
He'll be there, He'll be there,
When I'm all on my own, or I've lost my way,
He will always be there!

        CHORUS

3   When I'm down in the dumps, and things are looking bad,
He'll be there, He'll be there,
When I'm over the moon, (when I'm really glad!)
He will always be there!

        CHORUS

        LAST CHORUS:
        OH YEAH! (He'll be there!)
        OH YEAH! (He'll be there!)
        He will never leave me.
        I KNOW! (Oh I know!)
        HE CARES! (How he cares!)
        He's the only one I know who's always there!

HE'LL BE THERE

Words & Music by
MARK and HELEN JOHNSON

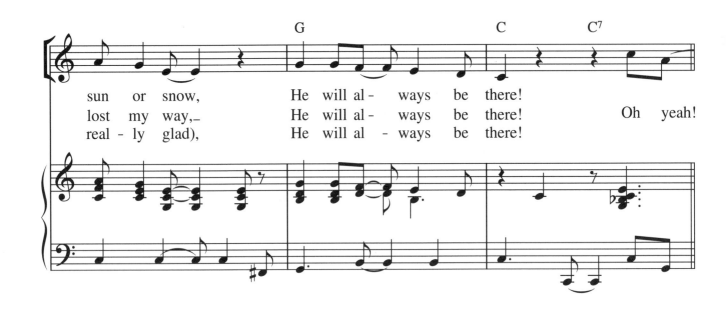

%: Chorus

(Sing echo in last Chorus only)

Harmony part (small notes) in last Chorus only

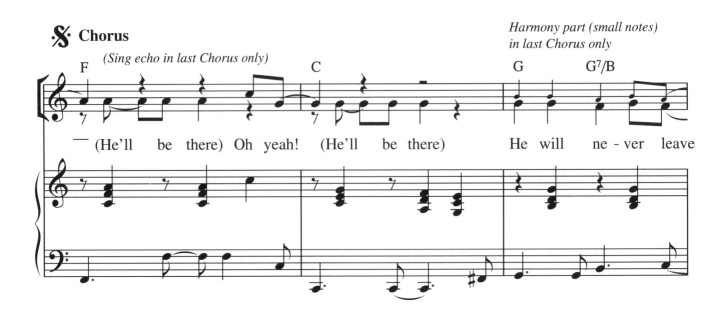

— (He'll be there) Oh yeah! (He'll be there) He will ne - ver leave

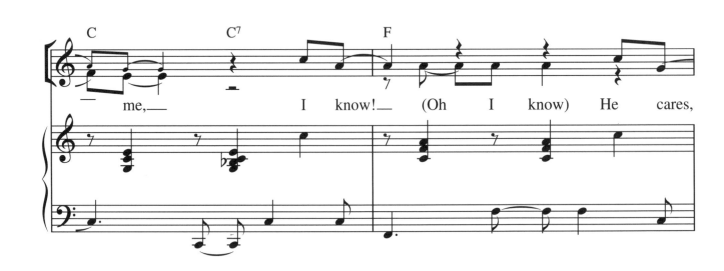

— me,___ I know!___ (Oh I know) He cares,

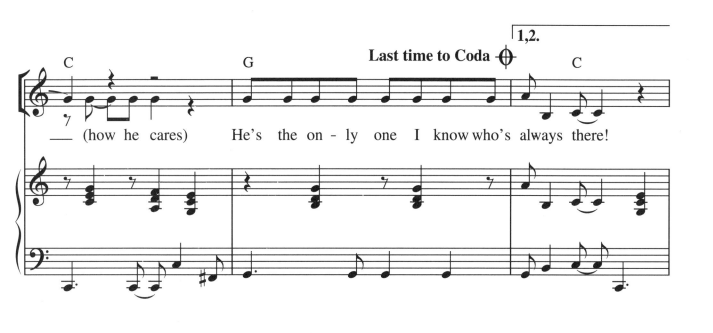

(how he cares) He's the on-ly one I know who's always there!

2.In the al-ways there! Oh yeah!
3.When I'm

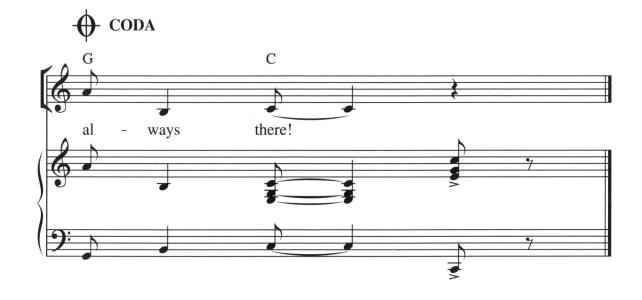

al - ways there!

WOULDN'T IT BE FUNNY...?!

1   Wouldn't it be funny if the sky were green,
    And the grass was spotty yellow!
    Wouldn't it be funny if the trees could walk,
    And the flowers and the plants could see!

    CHORUS   *Wouldn't it be strange!*
                   Wouldn't it be weird!
                   Wouldn't it be most peculiar indeed?!

2   Wouldn't it be funny if the fish could fly,
    And the cows played noughts and crosses!
    Wouldn't it be funny if the worms could sing
    And the ladybirds could laugh and cry!

    CHORUS

3   Wouldn't it be funny if we had three thumbs,
    And our feet were made of rubber!
    Wouldn't if be funny having 'see-through' skin
    And a pair of mouths instead of one!

    CHORUS

4   Wouldn't it be funny if we swam to school,
    And our teachers wore pyjamas!
    Wouldn't it be funny if we had new names
    And the children made up all the rules!

    CHORUS TWICE

    Wouldn't it be funny!
    Wouldn't it be funny!
    Wouldn't it be most peculiar indeed?!

WOULDN'T IT BE FUNNY ...?

Words & Music by
MARK and HELEN JOHNSON

In a quirky style ♩.=120

1. Would - n't it be fun - ny if the sky were green and the grass was spot - ty yel - low!
2. Would - n't it be fun - ny if the fish could fly and the cows played noughts and cros - ses!
3. Would - n't it be fun - ny if we had three thumbs and our feet were made of rub - ber!
4. Would - n't it be fun - ny if we swam to school and our teach - ers wore py - jam - as!

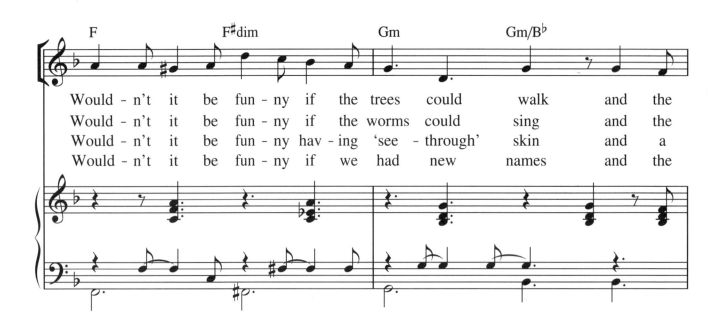

Would-n't it be fun-ny if the trees could walk and the
Would-n't it be fun-ny if the worms could sing and the
Would-n't it be fun-ny hav-ing 'see-through' skin and a
Would-n't it be fun-ny if we had new names and the

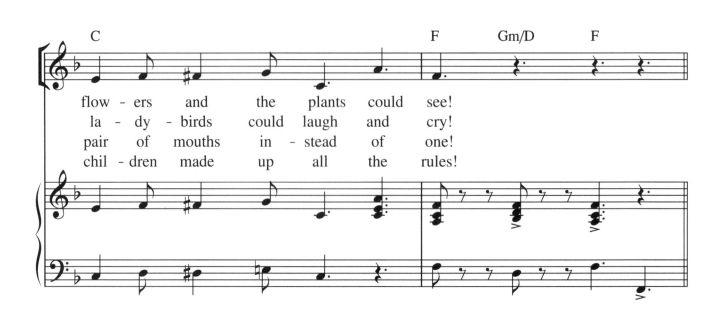

flow-ers and the plants could see!
la-dy-birds could laugh and cry!
pair of mouths in-stead of one!
chil-dren made up all the rules!

𝄋 Chorus

Would-n't it be strange! Would-n't it be weird!

50

GIVE IT ALL YOU'VE GOT!

Give it 1.., give it 2.., give it 1-2-3! (Repeat)

Give it 1.., give it 2.., give it 1-2-3! (Repeat)

CHORUS   *We are the children of .... school*,*
We take a pride in the things we do.
Learning together and having fun,
Who's for a good day? EVERYONE!

Give it 1.., give it 2.., give it 1-2-3! (Repeat)

1   Give it all you've got,
'Cause you've really got a lot!
Give it heart, give it mind,
Give it soul, don't stop!
(Repeat)

CHORUS

2   Everyone is special,
Everybody has gifts,
So we're gonna work together,
And we're gonna learn to give!
(Repeat)

Give it 1.., give it 2.., give it 1-2-3! (Repeat)

Repeat verse 1

Repeat verse 2

Give it 1.., give it 2.., give it 1-2-3! (Repeat)

CHORUS and '**Give it 1..,**' together, through to end

*see notes on song, page 54

GIVE IT ALL YOU'VE GOT!

Words & Music by
MARK and HELEN JOHNSON

> This 'dance' style song will require use of the backing track for effective performance.
> The four main elements of the song are included below for learning purposes.

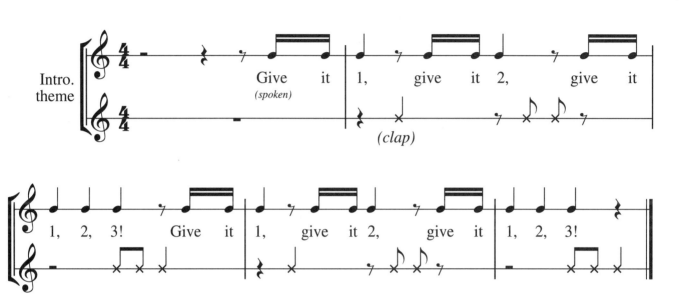

Intro. theme

Give it 1, *(spoken)* give it 2, give it *(clap)* 1, 2, 3! Give it 1, give it 2, give it 1, 2, 3!

Chorus

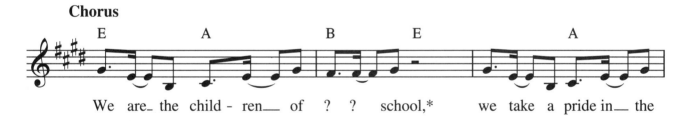

We are_ the child-ren_ of ? ? school,* we take a pride in_ the

things we do. Learn-ing_ to-geth-er,_ and hav-ing fun,

who's for_ a good day?_ EV'-RY-ONE!

Verse 1

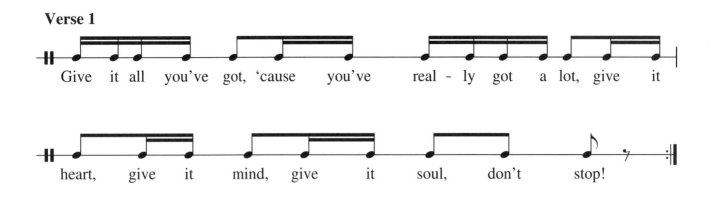

Give it all you've got, 'cause you've real - ly got a lot, give it
heart, give it mind, give it soul, don't stop!

Verse 2

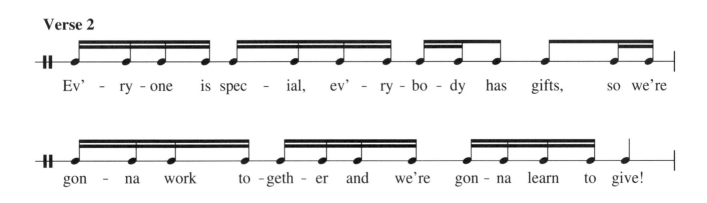

Ev' - ry-one is spec - ial, ev' - ry-bo - dy has gifts, so we're
gon - na work to -geth - er and we're gon - na learn to give!

*Variations on the rhythm and lyrics can be used in order to fit in the name of the school:

We are— the child - ren— of ? ? ? school

We are— the kids of— ? ? ? school,

We are— the kids of— ? ? ? ? school

We are— from ? ?— ? ? ? school,

We are— ? ? ?— ? ? ? ? school

For use with children in churches it is possible to adapt the first two lines of the chorus:
"We are the children of Sunday school, we're praising Jesus in all we do..." etc.

54

WELL DONE!

Version A

1
Well done!
You beat the lot,
Well done!
You came out tops,
Well done!
Congratulations,
You deserve the praises!

2
Well done!
You showed the crowd,
Well done!
You did us proud,
Well done!
Congratulations,
You deserve the praises!

3
Well done!
From all the school,
Well done!
To one and all,
Well done!
Congratulations,
You deserve the praises!

4
Repeat verse 1

Version B

1
Well done!
You did your best,
Well done!
We're so impressed.
Well done!
Congratulations,
You deserve the praises!

2
Well done!
You worked so hard,
Well done!
You hit the mark,
Well done!
Congratulations,
You deserve the praises!

3
Well done!
From all the school,
Well done!
You did it all,
Well done!
Congratulations,
You deserve the praises!

4
Repeat verse 1

Version A is intended for use in celebrating competitive successes - personal or corporate.

Version B is to be used where the success is one of personal/team effort or achievement, rather than for 'winning' at something.

WELL DONE!

Words & Music by
MARK and HELEN JOHNSON

With bounce! ♩=110

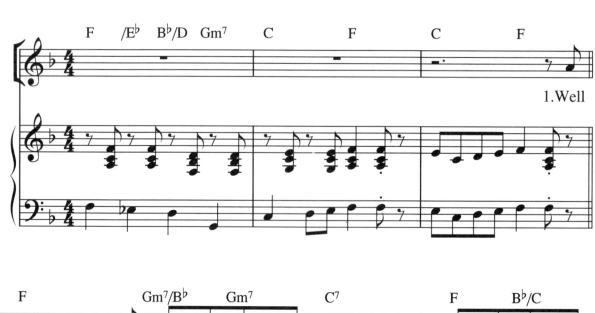

1.Well

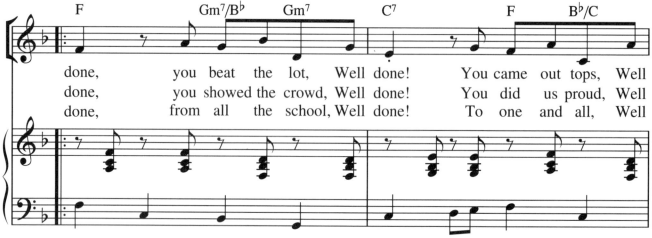

done,   you beat the lot, Well done!   You came out tops, Well
done,   you showed the crowd, Well done!   You did us proud, Well
done,   from all the school, Well done!   To one and all, Well

1,2.

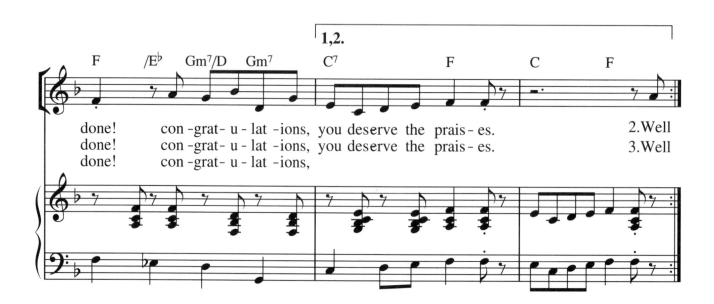

done!   con -grat- u - lat -ions, you deserve the prais- es.   2.Well
done!   con -grat- u - lat -ions, you deserve the prais- es.   3.Well
done!   con -grat- u - lat -ions,

you des -erve the prais - es!

4.Well
(Repeat verse 1)

1, 2, 3, 4!
(Spoken or percussive)

you des -erve the prais - es!

WELL DONE!

Version B - for recognition of personal/group effort or achievement,
as opposed to competitive success

1. Well done! You did your best,
   Well done! We're so impressed,
   Well done! Congratulations,
   You deserve the praises!

2. Well done! You worked so hard,
   Well done! You hit the mark,
   Well done! Congratulations,
   You deserve the praises!

3. Well done! From all the school,
   Well done, You did it all,
   Well done! Congratulations,
   You deserve the praises!

TODAY

1   Today is the day we've been given,
      To care for everyone,
      In all we do,
      In all we say,
      May this day be filled with kindness and with love.

2   INSTRUMENTAL

3   Repeat verse 1

TODAY

Words & Music by
MARK and HELEN JOHNSON

59

more songs for 'EVERY'...

season　　　　**day**　　　　**christmas**　　　　**easter**

bringing you the best children's songs for EVERY day of the year!

Each package in the series will provide you with:

- 15 original songs - catchy, memorable and great fun to sing!
- Piano music, melody and chords
- Photocopiable lyric sheets
- Cassette/CD with all songs sung by children
- Professionally arranged backing tracks for rehearsal and performance
- A tremendous resource for assemblies, topic work <u>and</u> concerts

The 'EVERY' series - popular with music advisors and non-specialists alike!

For details of other Out Of The Ark Music publications contact:

OUT OF THE ARK MUSIC
The School House, 15 Esher Green,
Esher, Surrey, KT10 8AA

Tel: (01932) 232250   Fax: (01932) 703010

ALSO AVAILABLE....

off to bethlehem

An exciting nativity musical comprising 9 catchy songs, which can be used individually or as a whole. Easy-to-use package includes teacher tips, stage directions, piano music, percussion parts, lyric sheets for photocopying.

This has proven to be one of the most popular publications in the Out Of The Ark Music catalogue.

Especially suitable for ages 5-9

it's a baby!

The christmas story with a difference! Told from the perspective of a weary innkeeper who finds he's in for a sleepless night. 9 new songs perfectly suited to younger voices, without compromising on musical quality. Simple rhyming narrative links and percussion parts are provided.

Funny, melodic and <u>very</u> singable!

Written specifically for 3-7 year olds

witnesses *by Margaret Carpenter*

Many years after the 'first' Christmas, Mary and Joseph, shepherds, kings, angels and stars all come back together as witnesses to the great event.

7 delightful songs, easy to learn and great fun to sing. Part-singing made surprisingly simple!

Best suited to ages 6-11

This timeless classic is now retold as a great new musical!

18 excellent songs in a wonderful variety of musical styles. Top quality package includes 96-page teacher's book (piano music, lyric sheets, casting tips, ideas for staging, props, etc), double cassette/CD with full backing tracks included. Full script also available.
Ideal for children aged 7-14